My Little Yellow Book

First steps in Bible reading

Leena Lane & Penny Boshoff

© Scripture Union 2003
First published 2003
Reprinted 2010
ISBN 978 1 85999 693 5

Scripture Union, 207–209 Queensway, Bletchley, Milton Keynes, MK2 2EB
Email: info@scriptureunion.org.uk
Website: www.scriptureunion.org.uk

Scripture Union Australia, Locked Bag 2, Central Coast Business Centre, NSW 2252
Website: www.su.org.au

Scripture Union USA, PO Box 987, Valley Forge, PA 19482
Website: www.scriptureunion.org

Scriptures quoted from the Contemporary English Version © American Bible
Society 1991, 1992, 1995. Anglicisation © British & Foreign Bible Society 1996. Used
with permission.

Illustrations: Jenny Tulip at Beehive Illustration Agency
Cover and internal design: Mark Carpenter Design Consultants
Additional material: Val Mullally (page 63); Rev Alison Gidney (page 19); 'Lydia' on
page 47 previously published in Let's Join In! Scripture Union © 1990

Typesetting: Servis Filmsetting Ltd, Manchester
Printed and bound by Tien Wah Press, Singapore

✒ Scripture Union is an international Christian charity working with churches
in more than 130 countries providing resources to bring the good news about Jesus
Christ to children, young people and families – and to encourage them to develop
spiritually through the Bible and prayer.

As well as a network of volunteers, staff and associates who run holidays, church-
based events and school Christian groups, Scripture Union produces a wide range
of publications and supports those who use the resources through training
programmes.

What's in this book?

How to use this book

When children are small, before they can read, it can be hard to know how to introduce the Bible to them. The *Tiddlywinks Little Books* offer a simple and enjoyable way to do so. Each book introduces Bible stories and truths through the lives of young children today. As they explore and discover and learn about the Bible in their day-to-day lives, they share their discoveries with us.

There isn't a "right" way to use *Tiddlywinks Little Books*. If you'd like to read something every day, each numbered page gives you a story and a prayer idea. Alternatively, you could read several pages in one go for a longer story. *Little Books* do not tie you to a certain date: use them as often as suits you and your child. Young children enjoy hearing stories again and again so don't feel you have to keep moving on or can only read a section once. There are extra pages too with ideas for activities, rhymes and crafts, and things for the children to do themselves. There is also a page for you, as you seek to introduce ideas about God and the words of the Bible to the children in your care.

You might like to set aside a time for using the *Little Books*, perhaps at bedtime or while you have a meal together. Or keep the book handy so you can use it anytime – on a bus journey, at a pause in a day of busy playing or while you're waiting for a visitor to call.

Children in their early years are growing faster and learning more than at any other time in their lives – an ideal time to take their "First steps in Bible reading".

*Day 31 onwards: we have kept the name 'Paul' throughout these pages to minimise confusion for the children. In the Bible, he is known as 'Saul' in these first few readings.

Meet Danny

This is Danny. He is almost four years old and he loves jumping! He jumps on his bed, and he especially likes jumping on his mum and dad's big bed. He jumps into his clothes in the morning and into his pyjamas in the evening. Gramps, Danny's grandad, calls him "Tigger" because he's so bouncy! Danny jumps a lot when Gramps is around. He's one of Danny's favourite big people!

Danny can't sit still for long – he loves racing around. His little sister Beth loves watching him. She's only eight months old. Danny loves having a little sister, although at first he thought she was a bit too noisy!

Danny's mum and dad go to work every day, so Danny goes to play at Sandra's house with another boy, Jamie. Sandra is their childminder.

And every morning Sandra takes Danny to nursery, which is very exciting.

Danny is learning about Jesus. He is finding out why people jump for joy at Easter! Do you want to find out too?

"Hello! I'm Tiddly Tamsin!
Look for me as you share this book!"

Danny at the farm

Danny went to visit a farm on Saturday with Gramps. They saw all kinds of animals: cows, sheep, piglets and a donkey! Danny raced up to the donkey and patted his nose. It felt really soft.

"Can I ride on the donkey?" asked Danny, feeling very excited. He had heard at church how Jesus rode on a donkey and he wanted to try it!

One of the farm workers fastened a saddle onto the donkey's back and lifted Danny up. He felt very high up and waved to the other people watching him.

"Wow!" said Danny. "It's great, sitting up here!"

On Palm Sunday, Jesus rode into the big city of Jerusalem on a donkey's back. Everyone waved and cheered. They threw branches from palm trees on to the ground in front of Jesus' donkey. Jesus was the new king everyone was waiting for.

Pray

Dear Jesus, I want to wave and cheer for you, too!

    Luke 19:28–40

2 Jesus is alive

Jesus on a donkey

King Jesus?

Do you like dressing up? Danny's friend, Krista, loves dressing up as a princess, with a long flowing dress and a crown. She always wants Danny to be a prince.

"But I don't want to be a prince!" says Danny.

"Be a king, then!" says Krista, throwing a long cloak and a big crown to Danny. He puts the cloak and crown on, and looks in the mirror.

"Mum, if Jesus was a king, did he wear a crown?" asks Danny.

"Not a golden one," says Mum. "Jesus was a different sort of king."

"Why?" asks Danny.

"Because Jesus didn't sit on a throne in a castle or a palace. He walked about talking to all the people and lived like us. He didn't have any money or fine clothes."

"So why do we call him a king?" asks Danny.

"It's because he's the most important king of all," says Mum. "He looks after us and he shows us how to live God's way."

Pray

Dear God, thank you for making Jesus our king.

A present for Jesus

What's your favourite smell? Strawberry yoghurts, or bananas, or maybe your bubble bath? What smell do you not like at all? Your brother's socks? Danny is not too sure about the smell of his sister Beth – sometimes she smells lovely and clean, but not when her nappy needs changing…

Can you think of a present that smells nice?

Jesus was once given a very smelly present. Jesus had gone to have dinner with a man called Simon. Suddenly Mary came into the room. She was the sister of Jesus' friend Lazarus. Mary did something very strange. She poured perfume over Jesus' head! It smelled lovely, though. Mary wanted to give Jesus the best present she could think of. He was very pleased with what she had done. It showed Jesus that she loved him very much.

Pray
Dear Jesus, I'd like to give you a special present too. What shall I give?

Mark 14:3–9

Danny buys a present

Danny wanted to buy his grandad a really special birthday present.

"Mum!" shouted Danny. "I've saved up three pounds in my money box! I'm going to buy something really nice for Gramps."

"Do you want to keep a bit to spend on sweets or stickers for yourself?" asked Mum.

Danny thought hard. "No!" he said. "I want to spend it ALL on Gramps. I think he's great!" Danny thought some more about what to buy. He knew Gramps would like some new goalkeeper gloves for when they played football together.

Mary wanted to spend all her money on a very special gift for Jesus. Other people thought she was silly when she bought some very expensive perfume and then poured it on his head. But Jesus knew why she did it. And he was pleased.

Pray

Dear God, it's a lovely feeling when we give someone a special present.

Thank you for all that you give to us.

Having a party

Have you ever planned a special party meal for your friends? Who did you invite?

Jesus had twelve special friends. Jesus knew he was going away soon so he wanted to have a special meal with them first.

Jesus got everything ready – he found a room to have the meal, he invited his best friends and got the food ready. He gave them some meat, some bread and some wine.

When his friends arrived, they all sat down around the table. Jesus said thank you to God for the food and then passed it round. It was good to be together one last time. Jesus would soon be going away. His friends didn't know that

he would be coming back again – but he did come back!

Pray

Dear Jesus, I'm sad that you had to go away, but very happy that you came back again!

Goodbye to a friend

Danny has lots of friends at nursery, but his very best friend
was Josh. They used to make dens together and pretend to go
looking for dragons in the park.

Last year Josh had to move to a new town.
Danny was sad, because he thought he might
never see Josh again. Before he left, Josh had
a big party to say goodbye to his friends.
Danny's mum took a photo of Danny and
Josh, to remind Danny of his old best friend.

Before Jesus had to go away, he asked his
special friends to come to a meal. He
asked them always to remember him. He
gave them some bread and wine.
As they ate and drank, Jesus told
them to think about him until he
came back.

Jesus' friends didn't have any
photos of Jesus. There were no cameras
then! But whenever they had a meal together with bread and
wine, they would remember Jesus.

Pray

Dear God, help us always to remember
Jesus.

Easter is coming

It was nearly Easter! Danny was very excited about it. Everyone at nursery was talking about how many Easter eggs they could eat.

"I bet I could eat four!" said Krista.

"Well, my big brother can eat ten!" said Jamie.

Danny had heard people talking about 'Good Friday' coming before Easter.

"Dad, is it called Good Friday because we can eat all our Easter eggs then?" asked Danny.

"No," said Dad. "You have to wait until Easter Sunday."

"But that's no good!" said Danny. "I can't wait that long. So why is it called Good Friday? What's so *good* about it?"

"It's because it's the day we remember Jesus giving everyone a really fantastic present," said Dad.

"What sort of present?" asked Danny.

"Something that lasts a lot longer than your Easter eggs!" said Dad. "Jesus showed us that God loves us for ever and ever!"

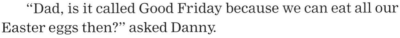

Pray

Dear Jesus, thank you for loving me so much. I love you too.

John 3:16

A very sad day

"But Dad," said Danny. "What exactly did Jesus do on Good Friday?"

"Well, it's very sad," said Dad. "But it's happy in the end, so don't worry! Jesus had done nothing wrong, but there were people who didn't like the things he said about God. They thought he was making it all up when he told them that God loved them all the time. He told them that God always wants to forgive us when we do wrong things."

"Like when I shout at you sometimes or hit my friends?" asked Danny.

"Yes," said Dad. "Jesus was taken away and put on a cross made of wood. Then he died. But before he died, he asked God to forgive everyone for being horrid to him."

"So Jesus *died*? That's terrible! I thought he was alive and my friend!" said Danny.

"You're right! That's the amazing thing," said Dad. "Jesus came alive again! And now we can be friends with God for ever!"

"Wow!" said Danny.

Pray

Dear God, thank you that Jesus came alive again and can be my friend.

Mark 15

Easter is here!

When Jesus had died on the cross, his body was taken and put in a cave. A very heavy stone was rolled in front of the door to the cave. It was very difficult to move. All his friends were very sad. They thought they would never see him again.

But on Sunday, when Mary went to the cave, she found something amazing. Jesus had gone! Where could he be? An angel had rolled away the heavy stone in front of the cave. Mary didn't know what to think. Then the angel spoke to Mary: "Don't be scared. Jesus is alive!"

Mary was so surprised and so happy. Could it really be true?

She soon found out for herself. Jesus came to see her and all his friends. Yes, Jesus really was alive again! Hooray!

Pray
Dear Jesus, thank you that you really are alive!

Matthew 28:1–10

Easter time

Colour in the face that shows how Jesus' friends felt when Jesus came into Jerusalem on the donkey.

Colour in the face that shows how Jesus' friends felt when Jesus died.

Now draw a face in the circle below to show how Jesus' friends felt when they found out that Jesus was alive again!

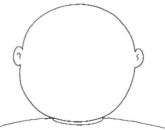

A very happy day

Danny still felt a bit sad that Josh had moved away. If only he could come back one day…

A long, long time after Josh moved house, Danny's mum had a phone call from Josh's mum. Danny rushed up to his mum as she put the phone down.

"Danny!" said Mum. "Josh is coming to visit us!"

Danny was so pleased! At last he would see his old friend again. They could go looking for dragons in the park and make dens in the garden again. Danny jumped around the room like a kangaroo – he was so excited!

Jesus' friends were really excited too, when Jesus came back to life again! They had been very sad when he went away. They thought they would never see him again. But now they were very happy!

Pray

Dear God, thank you for bringing Jesus back to his friends and to us!

John 20:19–20

It's amazing!

Do you know where butterflies come from?
    First, there's a caterpillar. It eats lots of green leaves and grows and grows.

Then it builds a cocoon around itself – a type of brown shell. It looks a bit like a small dead twig. No one would think there was anything inside. But inside the cocoon something amazing is happening... Very quietly, the caterpillar is turning into something beautiful. One day, the cocoon opens and out flutters a beautiful butterfly, stretching its new wings and flying high into the air.

When Jesus died, he was put in a dark cave. He stayed there for two days. Everyone thought he would never come out. But then an angel opened the cave and Jesus came out again – alive!

Butterflies are amazing, but Jesus is even more amazing – he came alive again and lives for ever!

Pray

Dear Jesus, it's amazing that you came alive again. Hooray!

Matthew 28:5–7   17

Danny's Easter eggs

It was Easter morning. "It's Easter! It's Easter!" shouted Danny. "Can I eat my Easter eggs now?" he asked his mum.

"Oh, Danny! You're up too early!" groaned Mum.

"But it's so exciting!" said Danny. "Mum, why do we have eggs at Easter? Did Jesus eat eggs?" asked Danny. He couldn't stand still, he was so excited.

"I'm not sure if Jesus ate eggs," said Mum. "But we have eggs at Easter because they remind us of new life. If a hen sits on her eggs, little chicks grow inside them and hatch out, leaving the shell behind. Out jump new little chicks! At Easter, we think about Jesus coming back to life."

"I know," said Danny. "Jesus sort of jumped out of that cave, didn't he?"

"Yes!" said Mum.

"Hooray! Now it's time to find my eggs!" said Danny.

Pray

Dear God, thank you for Easter eggs and for helping me to think about Jesus.

John 20:1–20

Going along the road

Here's a rhyme to share together. You might like to march around the room as you read it and shout "Jesus is alive!" each time you get to that line! The rhyme tells the story of when Jesus appeared to two of his friends as they were walking on the road to a town called Emmaus. This is what they might have said.

We have seen him, he's alive,
We have seen him, he's alive,
We have seen him, he's alive,
Jesus is alive!

Jesus walked the road with us,
Jesus walked the road with us,
Jesus walked the road with us,
We know he's alive!
We have seen him…

He sat down to eat with us,
He sat down to eat with us,
He sat down to eat with us,
And we know he's alive!
We have seen him…

He will always be with us,
He will always be with us,
He will always be with us,
Jesus is alive!
We have seen him…

Pray
Dear Jesus, I know you're always with me.
Help me to listen to you.

Luke 24:13–35

Josh is coming

Danny was very excited about his friend, Josh, coming to visit!

"He might look a bit different," said Dad. "You haven't seen him for a whole year."

"I still know what Josh looks like," Danny said to himself.

The train pulled into the station. The doors beeped as they opened. But where was Josh? Danny saw a boy with glasses and with trainers with lights flashing on the side. "No, that's not Josh," thought Danny. He kept on looking at the other passengers.

"Hello, Josh!" said Dad.

Why was Dad talking to that boy with glasses and calling him "Josh"?

Danny looked a bit closer. Then he realised – it *was* Josh after all! Hooray!

When Jesus came back to his friends, they didn't all recognise him at first. Some of his friends couldn't believe it was Jesus! But they soon found out that it really was him. Jesus had come back!

Pray

Dear God, I feel so happy when I see friends again after a long time away. Thank you that Jesus came back to see his friends again.

Hooray! Jesus is alive!

Have a happy time colouring this happy picture!

Going fishing

There's a big pond near Danny's home. Sometimes, on Saturday afternoons, Danny's mum takes Danny pond-dipping. Danny loves fishing about with his net. Sometimes he catches lots of pondweed but no fish!

Some of Jesus' friends were fishermen. They once went out fishing all night on the lake but didn't catch a thing.

In the morning, they saw a man standing at the water's edge. "Throw your net out on the other side of the boat," he said, "and you will catch some fish."

So the men did as he said and the nets were suddenly filled with fish! Not just one or two. Not even ten or twenty. There were more than a hundred fish in their net!

Peter knew at once that the man on the shore was Jesus! He had come back!

On the shore, Jesus had lit a fire, ready to cook some of the fish. It was a barbecue on the beach! Jesus and his friends shared a meal together once again.

Pray

Thank you, Jesus, for the food you give us.

Who's that on the shore?

Here's a rhyme to enjoy together. It tells
the story of Jesus appearing to his
friends on the shore of the lake.
One of you can read the first part
of each line, and the other one can
repeat the words, like an echo.

Fishing all night, fishing all night,
Wishing for fish, wishing for fish,
Nothing in my nets, nothing in my nets,
Where are the fish? Where are the fish?
Who's that on the shore? Who's that on the shore?
Can it really be? Can it really be?
Jesus is back! Jesus is back!
Cooking fish for me! Cooking fish for me!

Here's a fun way to pray.

    Cut out simple fish shapes from coloured paper. Draw
people or things on them to pray for, maybe your family and
friends. Put the fish in a net (a fruit or vegetable bag would
do). Take it in turns to "fish" one out. Say a prayer for each
one.

Pray

Jesus' friends had so much to tell him
when they saw him again. Tell Jesus about
what you've been doing today.

John 21:1–14

Do not worry

Danny had heard about Jesus coming alive again. But something was puzzling him. If Jesus was alive now, where *was* he?

"Mum!" asked Danny. "Why can't we see Jesus *now*?"

Danny's mum thought for a moment, "Well, Jesus really is alive, but he's gone to see someone very important now. He's gone to be with God in heaven!"

Mum told Danny what happened next.

"Jesus' friends were so pleased when Jesus came alive again! But Jesus still had to go somewhere important. He was going to heaven! That was where God, his Father, was waiting for him. Jesus said a 'goodbye' prayer with his friends. He asked God to be with them and look after them. Then Jesus went up to heaven in a cloud.

"Two angels appeared to tell Jesus' friends not to worry – Jesus would come back again one day. They were so pleased to hear that!"

Pray

Dear Jesus, you're coming back some day – I'm excited about that!

Acts 1:9–11

"See you again"

Danny had a great time when Josh stayed with him. But the time came for Josh to go home – back to his new home, away from Danny's house.

Danny felt a bit sad about that.

"Hey!" said Josh. "You can come and see me next!"

That made Danny feel a bit better. He liked the sound of that.

"I've even got a trampoline!" said Josh. "You can jump as much as you like at my house!"

"And Josh can come and see us again soon, too," said Danny's mum.

Danny waved goodbye to Josh as the train pulled out of the station.

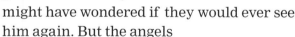

Do you think Jesus' friends felt a bit sad when they saw Jesus go to heaven? They might have wondered if they would ever see him again. But the angels told them that he would come back one day. That made them very excited!

Pray

Dear God, thank you that Jesus is coming back!

Acts 1:9–11

Feel the wind

Close your eyes and think about the wind. Imagine you are standing outside on a really windy day. It's a warm wind, blowing on your face. How does it feel? Can you make the sound of the wind?

Jesus promised his friends that when he went back to heaven, he would not leave them all alone. He would send a helper, the Holy Spirit, to be with them. The Holy Spirit came like a strong wind. No one could see it, but it blew over Jesus' friends as they met together in a room. They saw something which looked like flames of fire. They could suddenly say all sorts of words that they didn't know before. They began to tell everyone all about Jesus. The Holy Spirit gave them special power to tell others about Jesus. Wow!

Pray

Dear God, thank you for sending the Holy Spirit to be with us too.

Danny asks some more

Danny was thinking hard. He'd eaten all his Easter eggs a long time ago. He'd learnt about Jesus on Good Friday. He'd heard that Jesus had gone to heaven. But now he was a bit puzzled.

"Mum!" asked Danny at bedtime. "Has Jesus come back yet, like the angels told his friends he would?"

"Jesus hasn't come back yet, Danny," said Mum, "but he has sent his helper, the Holy Spirit, to be with us."

"Can we see the Holy Spirit?" asked Danny.

"No," said Mum. "But he's always there when we pray to God. And he helps us to do things which please God, like being kind to other people."

"Is the Holy Spirit everywhere? Even here with us?" asked Danny.

"Yes," said Mum.

"He must be *really* big then," said Danny. "How can God be *so* big?"

"Well," said Mum, "he's God, and God can do everything!"

Pray

Dear God, thank you that you are here with me now.

John 15:26–27

Danny's mum

Danny's friend Krista is very excited. Her mum is soon going to have another baby! Danny remembers when his mum had his baby sister, Beth. It was all very noisy in the house! Danny got a bit cross after a while, because Dad kept telling him to stop jumping around when Beth was asleep.

"Mum," asked Danny. "Do you like being my mum?"

"Of course!" laughed Mum. "I love being your mum! Even when you jump on me at six o'clock in the morning!"

Sarah, in the Bible, wanted to be a mum, but she couldn't have children for many years. Then, suddenly, God promised that she and Abraham would have a son! Sarah laughed. She wasn't sure whether to believe what God said. But she did have a baby boy and they called him Isaac. His name means "laughter"!

Pray
Dear God, thank you for all the grown-ups who look after me!

Genesis 18:1–15

Before you were born

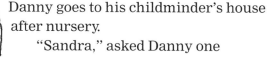

Danny goes to his childminder's house after nursery.

"Sandra," asked Danny one afternoon, "you're a bit like my mum, aren't you? I mean, you look after us when Mum's at work, you make us a drink if we're thirsty and you change Beth's nappies."

"But I'm not your mum," said Sandra. "Mums are something really special. They look after you right from the minute you're born, and before you are born, even, when you're growing inside their tummies."

"Like Krista's mummy's got a big tummy now?" asked Jamie.

"Just like that!" said Sandra. "And Krista's mummy already loves her baby, even though she hasn't seen it yet."

"And God does, too, doesn't he?" asked Danny.

"Yes," said Sandra. "He does!"

Danny thinks his mum is really special – he feels really happy when he sees her appear at the door to collect him from Sandra's house. He loves the big hugs she gives him too!

Pray

Dear God, thank you that you made me inside my mummy's tummy and you always loved me, even then!

Psalm 139:13–16

Families and friends

Think of the people in your family. Now think of a way you can show each person in your family that you love them. Maybe you can give them a hug and tell them they're great. Perhaps you could share your toys with them or ask if they would like your help. Maybe you can make a picture or card for them.

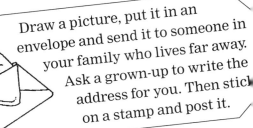

Draw a picture, put it in an envelope and send it to someone in your family who lives far away. Ask a grown-up to write the address for you. Then stick on a stamp and post it.

Make a prayer book. Find or take photos of the people in your family. Stick them carefully in a scrapbook. Then, when you look at the photos, you can talk to God about each person.

Dear God, take care of *Mum*,
and please look after *Dad*.
I know you love my *sister*
(though she drives me mad).
My *uncles* and my *cousins*
need to know you care,
And please remind my *auntie*
that you're always there.
Look after *Granpa* and my *Nan*,
I love them both, you see.
And God I want to thank you
For your love and care for me.

Make a treasure box
Does someone in your family have a birthday soon? Why not make them a treasure box covered in glittery jewels? Find a cardboard box with a lid (washing tablet boxes are good). Cover the box in silver or gold paper (or ask a grown-up to help you spray the box gold or silver). Then cut out different shapes of shiny coloured paper and stick these 'jewels' on the box.

Saturday football

Danny loves Saturdays. That's when his dad is at home! His dad works in the big city and gets home very late every evening. Danny's usually asleep by then. And sometimes he's asleep when Dad leaves for work in the morning. But on Saturdays, Danny sees Dad all day long!

"Dad!" said Danny, early on Saturday morning. "Can we go to the football with Reese?"

Danny and his dad, and Reese and his dad, sometimes go to the football match together. It's very noisy, but Danny and Reese love it!

Danny loves doing special things with his dad. It makes him feel very important.

In the Bible there's a story about Joseph. He loved doing things with his dad too. He knew his dad, Jacob, really loved him. His dad gave Joseph a fantastic coat to wear to show that he was really special. That made Joseph very happy and he wore his smart new coat all the time.

Pray

Dear God, thank you for special times with our families.

Genesis 37:1–11

Jesus talks to his dad

Danny knows that his dad loves him. Sometimes, when his dad is tired, or he's busy or watching television or reading the paper, Danny asks for a drink or something to eat. "I want it *now*, Dad!" shouts Danny.

Sometimes Dad gets cross and asks Danny to wait a minute. But he usually listens to Danny, even if he's sometimes a bit slow at getting him a drink or a snack!

Jesus loved talking to his dad. He often went to talk to him on his own when he felt sad or was in trouble. Jesus told his friends to talk to his dad too. Do you know who Jesus' dad is? It's God!

Jesus told us that we can talk to God like our dad, too. Jesus told us to talk to God about everything we need.

"Your dad already knows what you need before you ask him," said Jesus. He meant that God loves us very much and knows what will make us happy.

Pray

Dear God, thank you that we can call you "Dad" too, like Jesus did.

Matthew 6:8–9

Two pairs of twins

Do you have friends who are twins? Or maybe you are a twin yourself?

Danny has some friends who are twins – Lucy and Liam. They like very different things: Lucy loves dressing up and playing doctors. Liam likes painting and making dens.

Jacob and Esau were twin brothers, but they were very different too. Esau loved hunting and being outdoors. Jacob loved cooking and staying at home. Jacob and Esau were not always best friends. In fact, when they grew up, Jacob played a nasty trick on Esau and upset him a lot. Jacob stole something from his brother. Jacob went away for a long time. He thought his brother would always be very angry with him.

But, one day, Jacob was brave and came back to say sorry to Esau. Esau was very pleased to see his brother again and they gave each other a great big hug!

You can find out about Jacob and Esau being friends again in the Bible, Genesis 33:1–15.

Pray

Dear God, thank you that you make us all a bit different, even twins!

Genesis 25:19–34   33

Big brothers

Most of the time, Danny likes being a big brother to Beth, but he sometimes gets cross when Beth gets all the cuddles. And when she was born she got so many presents!

Do you remember that Joseph had been given a wonderful coat by his dad, Jacob? But Joseph's eleven brothers didn't get anything! They were very cross about it. In fact, they were so cross that they did something really horrid to Joseph – they sold him to some people who were going to a country far away. Joseph was very upset.

Many years later, the brothers said sorry to Joseph. Joseph was very pleased they could be friends again. He was really pleased to see them again, even though they had been horrid to him. They were his brothers, after all!

Pray
Dear God, help us to get on with each other in our families!

       Genesis 45:14

Big sister

Miriam had a very special job to do. She had to watch over her baby brother. Soldiers were going to take him away, so Miriam's mother made a special basket and put the baby in it. She made the basket waterproof and put it near the water's edge by the river. Miriam hid in the reeds to watch. She felt very proud to be a big sister, but she was a bit worried about her brother and hoped he would be OK.

Suddenly, Miriam heard voices. It was the princess from the palace! The princess found the baby in the basket and picked him up. "Oh no!" thought Miriam. "What's she going to do now?" But the princess was very kind. She wanted to look after the baby. Miriam jumped out of the reeds. "I know someone who can feed the baby," she said. And she ran to fetch her mother! Her mother was able to look after the baby until he was old enough to live in the palace with the princess. And the princess called the baby "Moses".

Pray

Dear God, thank you for little brothers and sisters. Help us to look after them.

Exodus 2:1–10

Martha and Mary

Danny's friend Lily has got two older sisters. They share a
bedroom and often argue about whose turn it is to tidy up!

Jesus had two friends who were sisters: Martha and Mary. He
went to visit them one day. Martha wanted to make Jesus very
comfortable and give him something nice to eat. She was too
busy to sit down. Her sister
Mary didn't do anything but
sit with Jesus and talk to
him. She felt very pleased
that Jesus had come to
their house.

Martha got more
and more tired with all
the hard work. She got a
bit cross about it and told
Jesus. "Tell Mary to
come and help me!" she
said.

But Jesus told her
to stop worrying. "Mary wants to
sit with me, so let her. Don't worry about so many things!"

The two sisters both wanted to see Jesus, but they had
different ways of making him feel welcome in their home.

Pray
Dear God, in our family, help us to love
each other.

                                                        Luke 10:38–42

Noah and his family

Danny's family was going on a journey to see Gramps. He lived a long way away. Danny's mum and dad packed the car with the things they would need: food for the journey, toys for Danny and Beth, nappies for Beth, a travel cot, the high chair, blankets and Danny's favourite Dalmatian soft toy dog called "Dot". There was hardly any room for the family!

Noah went on an even longer journey in a huge boat called the "ark". God had told Noah to build the ark to keep Noah and his family safe when the flood of water came. They filled the ark with animals! Noah's wife came too. And they had three sons called Shem, Ham and Japheth. They came aboard too and they all brought their wives with them. God would keep their whole family safe when the flood came.

Read about Noah again. Can you count up how many people were in his family?

Pray

Dear God, please look after me and my family.

My family

Danny always likes singing in the car when he goes on a long journey. He sings all the songs he has learnt at nursery. He would love to jump when he's singing action songs, but it's a bit hard when he's fastened into his car seat, so he just jigs about!

Danny's little sister, Beth, sometimes likes to join in too, giggling and trying to sing along to the songs. Danny likes it best when his whole family sings: Mum, Dad, Beth and him. It gets really noisy and it makes him really happy!

Danny loves singing at church too, especially songs with actions like "If I were a butterfly, I'd thank you, Lord, for giving me wings". Of course, Danny's favourite line is, "If I were a kangaroo, I'd *hop, hop, hop* right up to you!" Everyone laughs when they get the actions a bit mixed up! When everyone's singing together, Danny thinks church feels a bit like a really big family.

Pray

Dear God, thank you for our family at home and our friends at church.

    Psalm 133

Danny's decision

"I'm going to Sandra's, but I'm not going to nursery," Danny announced.

"Oh! But you usually have fun there," said Mum. "Sandra will be there to take you."

"Jack is horrible to me. He won't let me play with him and Krista. He messed up my puzzle and he pushed me over. So I'm not going!"

Mum gave Danny a hug. "It's horrid when people aren't kind to us," she said. "Come on, I'll tell you a story on the way to Sandra's."

"Paul wasn't a kind man at all. He was especially nasty to Jesus' friends. One day he was planning to do more horrid things when he saw a flash of light. He fell down and hid his eyes. Then he heard a voice. The voice said, 'Paul, why are you being horrid to me?' Who could it be? It was Jesus! From then on, Jesus became Paul's best friend."

Pray

When people are horrid and make me cry, I know I can talk to you, Jesus. You're my best friend.

Acts 9:1–6*
*see page 2

Danny changes his mind

Mum and Danny arrived at Sandra's house.

"I think I will go to nursery today," Danny said, "but I'm not going to play with Jack."

Mum helped Danny take off his coat, "Do you know, I think Jesus' friends would know how you feel. They didn't want to be friends with Paul because they knew he did horrid things. Jesus sent a message in a dream to his friend, Ananias. Jesus asked Ananias to go to Paul's house to help him. But Ananias didn't want to go at all.

"'Paul is horrid to anyone who is friends with you, Jesus,' he said.

"But in the dream Jesus said, 'You must go Ananias, because Paul is my friend now and I want him to help lots of other people.'

"What do you think Ananias did?"

Danny thought for a moment, "I think he went to help Paul."

Pray

Sometimes it's hard to be friends with people who are horrid to me. Please help me to be kind to them, Jesus.

     Acts 9:10–15

People who help

"What does 'encouraging' mean?" Danny asked Dad. "Jo at church said Jesus' friend Barnabas was encouraging."

"Well," said Dad, "do you remember getting stuck at the top of the big slide at the adventure park last week?"

Danny nodded. On the ground it had looked great fun. But at the top it had been really scary. He had tried to go back down the steps but there were too many big children in the way.

"I couldn't reach you," Dad said, "so I talked to you about your slide at home until you felt better about going down. I knew you could do it. I was *encouraging* you."

Danny looked puzzled, "Did Barnabas help people down slides?"

Dad smiled, "No, but when Jesus' friends were feeling scared or not sure how to do what Jesus wanted, Barnabas talked to them and helped them."

Pray

Who encourages you? It might be your mum or dad or someone at nursery. Say thank you to God for them.

Barnabas calls for help

Have you ever had to ask for help? Yesterday, Danny found Beth halfway up the stairs. The stair gate had been left open and she had crawled through and started climbing up. Danny knew he couldn't carry Beth down and he knew it was dangerous for her to be on the stairs, so he shouted for his mum to come quickly.

Barnabas had to get help too. There were so many people wanting to hear about Jesus.

"I can't help these people on my own," thought Barnabas. "I know, I'll ask Paul."

He couldn't shout for Paul to come because Paul lived a very long way away. There weren't any phones or postmen to deliver letters to people in those days, so Barnabas set out on the long journey to find Paul himself. He was so happy when he found Paul. Paul was happy to go with Barnabas and help him. Now all the people would hear about Jesus!

Pray

Draw a picture of the person who tells you about Jesus. Get a grown-up to write "Thank you Jesus for ... (*add in name*)" at the top.

Acts 11:25–26

Show Barnabas the way

Barnabas needs Paul's help to tell people about Jesus. He is setting out on a long journey to find Paul. He isn't sure which road to take. Can you help him find the right road to Paul's house?

Timothy

Timothy lived a long time ago,
With his mum and his dad and his gran.
Mum and Gran told him all about Jesus.
"He's the best friend of all," said Gran.

Tim was only a boy then,
  you see,
Just a little bit older than
  you.
But he knew that God
  really loved him
And the stories of Jesus
  were true.

One day a man called Paul came by.
"Come with me, and don't be shy.
Tell the stories of Jesus to all you meet.
You can do it. Just give it a try."

So, Tim and Paul went far and wide,
Over sea and mountains tall,
And everyone heard about Jesus
And how he's the best friend of all.

Pray
Dear Jesus, I'm young like Timothy. I'm
glad you want to be friends with me, too.

Acts 16:1–5

Danny gets a letter

"FFLUPP" went the letters through the letterbox. Dad went to pick them all up.

"Oh look! There's one for you, Danny!" he called.

He gave Danny the letter. Danny looked at the envelope. Who could have sent him a letter? He opened it quickly. Inside there was a drawing.

Mum looked over Danny's shoulder, "How lovely, Josh has drawn you a picture and he's written his name. Look. J – o – s – h."

Timothy got a letter too. His friend Paul had moved away. Timothy missed Paul but he loved getting letters from his friend. Timothy's letter from Paul said, "Well done, Timothy, for loving Jesus. Keep telling others about him. Don't be scared. Love, Paul."

Danny has drawn a picture of himself jumping on the bed. He's going to send it to his friend Josh. You could draw a picture and send it to a friend too!

Pray

Who is your friend? Say their name at the end of this prayer.

"Thank you, Jesus, for my friend ...."

2 Timothy 1:3–8

A new boy at nursery

Have you ever been somewhere new where you didn't know anyone? Did you feel a bit scared? Did you want someone to be friends with you?

Last week, a new boy came to Danny's nursery. He looked around. All the children were busy playing. They were all too busy to play with him. He felt scared and lonely. Then he saw some children doing puzzles. One of the boys looked up and smiled at him. The new boy felt better. Can you guess who smiled at him? Yes, it was Danny!

Jesus' friend Paul had gone to a new town. He didn't know anyone there. One morning he went for a walk by the river. A woman called Lydia was there with her friends. She was very kind to Paul and loved hearing about Jesus. Lydia became Paul's new friend.

Pray

Jesus, going to new places makes my tummy flutter but seeing friendly faces makes me feel much better.

Acts 16:13–14

Lydia

Here are Lydia and her friends.
(Hold one hand upright and wriggle fingers.)
Here is the flowing river.
(Lay other hand flat and ripple fingers.)
They love to sit upon its banks,
(Actions as before.)
And pray and talk together.

Here comes Paul with his three friends,
(Move four fingers along.)
Down to the flowing river.
(Ripple fingers of other hand as before.)
They join the women on the banks,
(Hold hands with palms facing and wriggle fingers.)
And sit and talk together.

Paul talks of his friend, Jesus.
(Hold up forefinger.)
Lydia listens well.
(Cup ears with hands.)
Then she says, "I'd like Jesus
To be my friend as well."

Lydia is happy,
(Smile.)
Jesus is her friend.
(Cross hands over chest.)
"Come and stay with me," she says
(Beckon with forefinger.)
To Paul and his three friends.
(Hold up four fingers and then cover them with the other hand.)

47

Danny's new friend

When Lydia heard Paul's stories about Jesus she became a friend of Jesus too.

"I'm so glad you told me about Jesus," she said. "Please come to my house today."

So Lydia took her new friend Paul to her house. They had a wonderful time talking together about Jesus.

Look who has come to play at Danny's house today. It's the new boy at the nursery. His name is Ben. Ben and Danny have been great friends ever since Ben arrived at the nursery. Ben makes Danny laugh. They always sit together at story time. Danny told Ben all about the spaceship models he and his dad made from boxes and foil. "Why don't you come to my house?" he asked Ben. "We can make some together."

Danny and Ben had great fun making models. Can you see what they've made?

Pray
Do you have a special friend? What do you like about them? Tell Jesus.

Acts 16:15

Danny goes to tea

"Is it time to go yet?" Danny asks Sandra.

"Soon," says Sandra. "Why don't you put your coat and shoes on?"

Danny is very excited because he's going to tea at Ben's house today. A little while later he and Sandra walk up the path to Ben's house. Ben is at the window. As soon as he sees Danny coming he rushes to open the door.

"Hi, Danny! Come on. Let's play!"

Ben runs upstairs and Danny follows close behind.

I wonder what Ben and Danny are up to? Can you see?

Jesus' friend Paul made tents. Paul's tents were bigger than the one that Danny and Ben made. Paul sold his tents to make money. One day he met some new friends, Priscilla and Aquila. They made tents too. And they were friends of Jesus. Paul went to stay with his new friends. They worked together. And they told lots more people about Jesus.

Pray

Hello God, my special friend is...................

We like to play .... together.

Acts 18:1–4

Danny is worried

Danny has been playing with his new friend Ben. He loves going to Ben's house. They have such fun. But today, Danny looks sad.

"What's wrong?" asks Mum. "Didn't you have fun with Ben today? You didn't argue, did you?"

Danny shakes his head. Then he asks Mum, "Will Ben go away too, like Josh did?"

"I don't know," says Mum. "It was sad when Josh went, wasn't it? But Josh is still your friend and you send each other letters. I don't think Ben will move away, but if he did he would still be your friend."

Priscilla and Aquila were very sad when their friend Paul had to leave. Paul sent them letters to let them know how he was. Priscilla and Aquila soon made a new friend. His name was Apollos. Priscilla and Aquila invited Apollos to their house. They had a great time talking about their friend Jesus.

Pray

Friends talk, friends share,
friends laugh, friends care,
Friends play, friends run.
Thank you, Jesus, friends are fun!

Acts 18:19–26

First steps in Bible reading
The *Tiddlywinks* range of Little Books

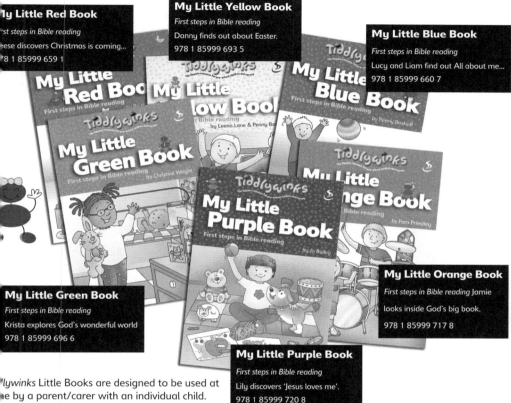

My Little Red Book

First steps in Bible reading

eese discovers Christmas is coming...

8 1 85999 659 1

My Little Yellow Book

First steps in Bible reading

Danny finds out about Easter.

978 1 85999 693 5

My Little Blue Book

First steps in Bible reading

Lucy and Liam find out All about me...

978 1 85999 660 7

My Little Green Book

First steps in Bible reading

Krista explores God's wonderful world

978 1 85999 696 6

My Little Purple Book

First steps in Bible reading

Lily discovers 'Jesus loves me'.

978 1 85999 720 8

My Little Orange Book

First steps in Bible reading Jamie

looks inside God's big book.

978 1 85999 717 8

lywinks Little Books are designed to be used at
e by a parent/carer with an individual child.
ed to the themes covered in the *Tiddlywinks* Big
ks, children can discover and learn about the
e and share their discoveries with you.
re are 50 first steps in Bible reading pages in
a book, with a story for each day and extra
vity pages of fun things to do. Children will love
oring the Bible with child characters Lucy and
n, Reese, Danny, Krista, Lily and Jamie.
64pp £3.99 each (Prices subject to change)

can order these or any other *Tiddlywinks* resources

our local Christian bookstore

ripture Union Mail Order:
elephone 01908 856006

nline: log on to
ww.scriptureunion.org.uk/tiddlywinks
order securely from our online bookshop

> 66 When the Big Books are used in conjunction with
> the Little Books, children and adults encounter an
> attractive mixture of stories and activities that will
> encourage everybody to know and trust in Jesus. 99
>
> **Diana Turner,**
> **Editor of *Playleader* Magazine**

The flexible resource for pre-school children and carers

Also now on sale!
Say and Sing. Glitter and Glue. Make and Do.

Danny's riddle

Danny heard a special rhyme in story time at nursery today. It's a riddle, which means you have to guess what the rhyme is about. Danny got it right. See if you can guess too. As you listen to the rhyme, look at the pictures, then point to the one the rhyme is about.

Look up, in the sky.
What do you see
Way up high?

It doesn't speak,
It doesn't shout,
Yet everyone knows when it is out.

It rises up
From way down low,
Then leaves the sky with a wonderful glow!

It's something bright,
It's something hot,
It's something round which shines a lot.

God put it there,
Just to show
How great he is, so we would know!

It's big and warm and bright and fun.
Do you know what it is?
Yes, it's the SUN.

Pray

I love the sun, it's bright and hot,
You made it God, thanks a lot!

Psalm 19:1–6

What's the weather like today?

Make a weather chart
Take a rectangular piece of paper.
Draw different weather in each
corner. Make an arrow pointer out of
black card and fix it in the middle of
your paper with a paper fastener.

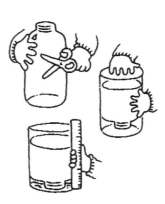

Measuring rain
Find out how much it rains. Take a
plastic juice bottle. Get a grown-up to
help you cut it in half. Turn the top
half upside down and place in the
bottom half. Use a ruler and a thick
waterproof pen to mark centimetre
measurements on the side of the
bottle. Now place your rain bottle
outside. When it has rained, go and
check how much rain is in your
bottle.

Wind decorations
There are lots of ways of making wind
decorations: twist pieces of tin foil
and thread string through the top,
paint pasta tubes and thread them on
to string, cut out lots of pieces of
shiny paper and thread them on to
string. When you have made your
decorations, hang the strings from
trees in your garden, or near a window
in your room, and watch and listen to
what the wind does with them.

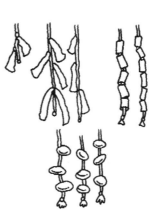

53

Sunny days

"Time to get up," said Mum, opening the curtains. The sun streamed in through the windows. It was warm and bright. It made Danny want to get up and play outside.

"Hooray!" shouted Danny, jumping up and down on his bed. "I like sunny days best! I'm going to play outside all day in the paddling pool and have ice-creams."

Mum laughed, "We'll see about the ice-cream! Come on, let's get you dressed."

What clothes should Danny wear today?

What else does he need to go out in the sun?

Later that day, Danny ran into the kitchen.

"I'm glad God made the sun, Mum," he panted. "But I think he made it too hot!"

"What a good job God made cool water!" said Mum, handing him a glass.

"Did God make ice-cream too?" Danny asked hopefully.

"I'm sure it was his idea!" Mum said, going to the freezer.

Pray

Thank you God for warm, sunny days.

Psalm 19:4–6

Danny at the seaside

Every year Gramps takes Danny to the seaside. They take a picnic and Gramps' binoculars so they can watch the boats go by. There are always big tankers, ferries, small tugs and fishing boats.

Today there are lots of smaller boats. "It's a nice windy day for those sailing boats!" says Gramps.

"Why is it nice if it's windy?" Danny asks.

"Well, sailing boats need the wind to make them go. In the old days all boats had sails. If it wasn't windy the boats couldn't sail. But when it was windy they would go really fast. Jesus' friend Paul used to go on long journeys by boat. He knew how dangerous the wind could be. If it was too strong it could blow the boat onto rocks."

Look out of your window. Is it a windy day? How can you tell?

Pray

I know God made the wind to blow clouds across the sky, to bend the tall, tall trees and make my small kite fly. Thank you, God!

Acts 27:7–20

Paul's dangerous journey

"When Jesus' friend Paul went on the boat, was he scared when it got very windy?" Danny asked Gramps.

"No, not even when the storm was so bad that the sailors were up day and night trying to save the ship from crashing. God sent an angel to Paul. 'Don't be afraid, Paul,' said the angel. 'God wants you to tell the Emperor in Rome about Jesus. So God will save you and all the other people on the boat.'

"Paul told everyone what God had promised. The next day the boat was near land. But the storm was so strong that the ship was falling apart. The people who could swim jumped in and swam to the shore. The others held onto large pieces of wood and floated to the shore. Everyone got safely to the dry land, just as God had promised."

Pray

Hello God, I'm glad that you kept Paul and his friends safe in the storm.

Acts 27:21–44

Rain, rain go away

"I hate rain," said Danny, with his nose to the window.

"I like rain!" said Gramps.

"Why?" asked Danny, looking surprised.

"Because rain fills the rivers, so that we have water to drink," Gramps explained. "Rain falls on the farmers' fields and makes the crops grow, so we have food to eat. And rain makes the grass grow, so the cows can eat and so they can make milk and cheese and yoghurt for us."

"And burgers!" added Danny.

Long ago, God told the king that there would be no rain for three years. It was a sad time. The grass and vegetables died because there was no rain. And the sheep and goats couldn't make milk because they didn't have grass to eat. All the people were hungry and thirsty. Then, one day, God sent his special messenger, Elijah, to tell the king that rain would come soon. And it did start to rain! And then it rained and it rained and it rained!

Pray

Dear God, I'm glad you made rain because......

1 Kings 18:1–2

Pitter patter raindrops

Have you been outside when it's started to rain? What did you do?

Dad and Danny were walking home from the park. "We'd better hurry," Dad said, "it's going to rain."

"How do you know?" Danny asked.

"I can see from the clouds," said Dad. "Look, can you see those dark clouds?"

Danny nodded.

"Dark clouds are rain clouds. The wind is blowing them this way, so the rain will be here soon," Dad warned.

A moment later Danny felt a raindrop.

"Let's run!" said Danny. So they did!

God's special messenger, Elijah, had to run home in the rain. He had told the king that God would send rain. Then he had gone up the mountain to ask God for rain. When he saw one tiny cloud he knew that God had answered his prayer. Soon the sky was covered in black rain clouds and it began to rain! Then it poured! Elijah got very wet!

Pray

Talk to God about a time that you got wet in the rain.

1 Kings 18:41–46

Crunchy grass?

One morning, everything outside had turned silvery white.

"Hooray, it's snow!" Danny shouted.

"No, it's not snow," said Dad. "It's frost." Danny looked disappointed.

"Frost is good fun too," Dad said. "We can go out after breakfast to explore."

And that's just what they did. Dad showed Danny the silvery patterns on a fallen leaf. Then they found a glittery spider's web, sparkling in the sun.

"Frost is like icing!" exclaimed Danny. "And it makes the grass crunchy!"

Dad and Danny walked round and round making footprints in the grass.

"How did everything turn white while I was asleep?" Danny asked. "Is it magic?"

"No, it's much more exciting and wonderful!" said Dad. "It's the way God planned it. God made the world so that some places get very cold in winter. And God knows that drops of water freeze into these lovely patterns when it gets very cold."

"God is very clever!" Danny decided.

Pray

Thank you God for crispy, crunchy, frosty days.

Psalm 147:15–18

59

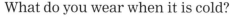

A snowy day

What do you wear when it is cold?

It snowed in Danny's town last night. There is just enough snow for Danny to make a small snowman. It is very cold outside. What is Danny wearing to keep warm?

Did you notice that Danny's hat and scarf match? Danny and his mum chose them at the shop. Danny likes them because he chose them and because they keep his ears and neck warm! Danny's mum works hard to earn money so that she can buy clothes for Danny and his sister.

There was a woman in the Bible just like Danny's mum. She worked very hard to make sure her children had warm clothes so they wouldn't get cold in winter. When winter came, her children were very glad they had thick, cosy clothes to wear.

Pray

Thank you God for cosy clothes that keep me warm and snug,

And thank you for my family – I'll give them each a hug!

Proverbs 31:13,21,28–29

God's beautiful promise

Have you ever seen a rainbow? Danny saw one yesterday. It was very beautiful. But it didn't last very long. It lasted just long enough for Gramps to tell Danny the story of the rainbow.

"Long, long ago, God asked his friend Noah to build a boat big enough for Noah, his family and two of every kind of animal, bird and insect. When they were safely inside, God made it rain until the whole earth was covered with water. Then the rain stopped and the flood went down. God said, 'Come out Noah! I promise I will never send so much rain ever again.' Noah and his family and the animals came out onto dry ground. When Noah looked up, he saw a beautiful arch made of many colours high in the sky. 'I've made a rainbow, Noah,' God said, 'so that I will always remember my promise to you.'"

Pray

Thank you, God, for making the rainbow and for keeping your promise.

Genesis 9:8–17

Rainbow colours

Danny is painting a rainbow.
But he can't remember all the
colours. Can you help him?
What colours does he need
to make a rainbow?

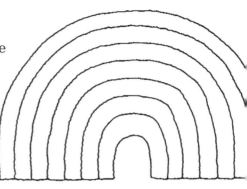

Here's a rhyme about
the colours of the rainbow.
Put up a finger every time
you hear a colour.

God started with red, and orange came next,
Followed by yellow and green.
Then he chose blue, and violet too.
What's he making? What could it be?

God made it up high like an arch in the sky,
Using the sun and the rain.
God said, "Look above, it's a sign of my love
That I'll never flood earth again."

Can you guess what it is, God's promise up high?
Yes, the rainbow! God's colourful arch in the sky!
But I've left out a colour.
Can you guess? Do you know?
It's a beautiful colour called 'indigo'.

How many colours did you count?

Pray
Dear God, my favourite colour is...............
Thank you for making the colour...............

Genesis 9:12–13

Understanding children's grief

The group of mourners looked out at the young child skipping around in the garden. "He doesn't even realise what has happened!" exclaimed one adult.

So often we can wrongly jump to the conclusion that children aren't grieving because they don't handle their grief in the same way as we do.

A child with a difficult task, perhaps a fairly complex jigsaw puzzle, will leave the task after a while and do something very different, returning to encounter it again later. When young children face a difficult challenge they generally handle it in small chunks – naturally sensing when they are no longer able to concentrate adequately on the task. It seems they handle grief in this way too. When the pain is too overwhelming they will turn their attention to something else for a while.

Realising this, we must not underestimate the intensity of the child's grieving. We need to be there respectfully – a comforting presence, reflecting the child's feelings, helping them to realise that in time the sad feelings won't feel so strong; answering questions and, when appropriate, remembering happy times.

Young children may not fully understand the concept of death, but they will still experience the loss of the presence of the loved one. They are also very aware of the pain in other people and instinctively know that something very sad has happened.

Like adults, it is not only human death that causes grief. Other situations, such as the death of a pet, ill health, beginning school, or moving to a new neighbourhood can bring a tremendous sense of loss to a child. Family friends and other carers have a very important role in supporting the child emotionally during times of loss. At such times the child needs loving support, and to be able to grieve in their own childlike, but very real, way.